I SPY
FOR BOYS!

Welcome to

I SPY
FOR BOYS!

GOOD LUCK!

I SPY with my little eye, something beginning with...

F

is for

FIRE
TRUCK!

I SPY with my little eye, something beginning with...

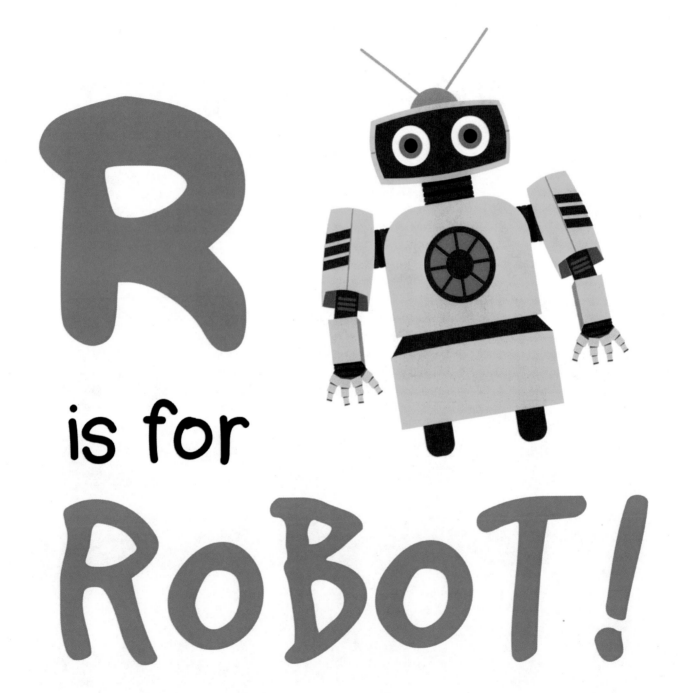

R

is for

RoBoT!

I SPY with my little eye, something beginning with...

V is for VOLCANO!

I SPY with my little eye, something beginning with...

B is for

BINOCULARS!

I SPY with my little eye, something beginning with...

K
is for
KING!

I SPY with my little eye, something beginning with...

H

is for

HELICOPTER!

I SPY with my little eye, something beginning with...

W is for WOLf!

I SPY with my little eye, something beginning with...

E

is for

ELF!

I SPY with my little eye, something beginning with...

S

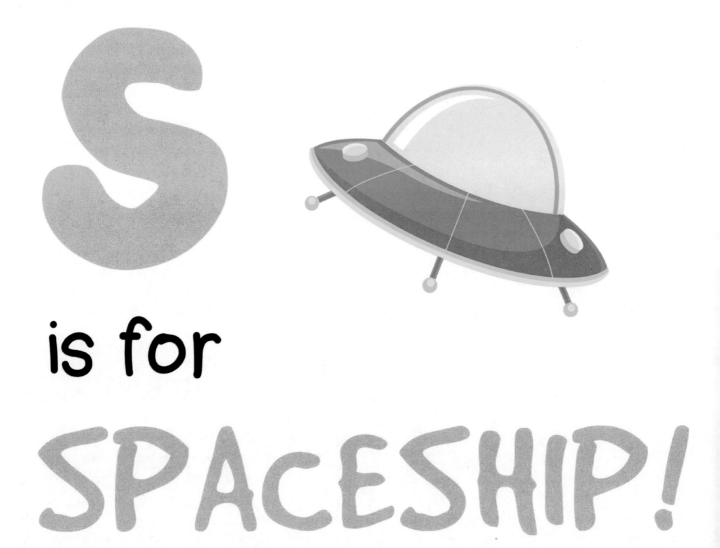

is for

SPACESHIP!

I SPY with my little eye, something beginning with...

T
is for
TIGER!

I SPY with my little eye, something beginning with...

G is for GUITAR!

I SPY with my little eye, something beginning with...

J

is for

JACK IN THE BOX!

I SPY with my little eye, something beginning with...

P

is for

PAINT!

I SPY with my little eye, something beginning with .

A is for
AXE!

I SPY with my little eye, something beginning with...

D is for DOG!

I SPY with my little eye, something beginning with...

C
is for
CRAB!

I SPY with my little eye, something beginning with...

M

is for

MONSTER TRUCK!

THE END!

Made in the USA
Las Vegas, NV
07 September 2023

77207366R00024